BAROQUE KEYBOARD PIECES

BOOK I

Edited by Richard Jones

The Associated Board of the Royal Schools of Music

CONTENTS

INTRODUCTION

Baroque Keyboard Pieces is a graded anthology, in five books, of the keyboard music of the period 1600–1750. It offers, taken as a whole, a fairly representative selection of the forms, styles and composers of that period, and aims to show how the music can be played stylishly, whether on the piano or on old instruments. A further aim has been to include pieces that are tuneful and memorable in the hope that the task of learning them will be enjoyable as well as instructive. For the same reason each book contains well-known as well as unfamiliar pieces. On the other hand, minor composers are sometimes more liberally represented than the great names in order to spread the knowledge of much fine and under-played music. The order of contents within each book is very loosely chronological: the selected pieces are arranged in groups according to source, date and nationality. An editorial note at the end of each piece gives a brief account of the source and text, remarks on the composer and the form or type represented at its first appearance in the volume concerned, and assistance in specific matters of interpretation. A few more general notes on the interpretation of Baroque keyboard music are given here.

Baroque music, in general, contains fewer performance indications than the music of later periods, for a good deal was left to the taste and sensibility of the player. This area of freedom was limited by the requirements of the *style* in which the music was written: hence we talk of 'stylish' playing. Some acquaintance with the style of the period and with various associated performance conventions that were widely understood at the time is therefore a prerequisite of effective interpretation. These matters are outlined briefly under the following headings.

Forms and Types The keyboard forms and types of the period vary in difficulty. For this reason the earlier books of this anthology contain predominantly keyboard dances, illustrative or character pieces, and preludes. The more difficult fugal, toccata and variation types occur with increasing frequency in the later books.

By far the most common form in the earlier books is *binary dance form*, which was almost universal in keyboard dances and often used on a larger scale in non-dance music, as in the Sonatas of Domenico Scarlatti or some of the Preludes from Bach's *Well-Tempered Clavier*. A binary piece is in two halves both of which are repeated. The first half often modulates to the dominant or relative major; the second half, known in French music as the *reprise*, returns to the tonic. *Rounded binary form*, in which the first strain is repeated at the close, eventually led to Classical sonata form (see Arne's Gavotte in B flat, Bk III, p.62). Longer binary pieces often have a *rhyming close*: the concluding sentence of the second half matches that of the first half, except in key. Compare, for example, the last six bars or so of each half of Mattheson's Air in A (Bk III, p.42). After both halves of a binary piece have been repeated, the closing sentence may be played again. This is known in French music as the *petite reprise*. It is usually indicated by the sign ⁒ , as in Louis Couperin's Minuet in C (Bk II, p.12), but if the composer wishes to vary the sentence, he will write the repeat out in full: compare, for example, bb.17–24 and 25–32 of le Roux's Passepied in F (Bk II, p.26).

Binary dances are often combined in pairs of the same type — see Clérambault's Minuet I & II, for example (Bk II, p.27) — the second half being repeated after the first, giving rise to an overall ABA da capo structure. Or an alternating scheme may operate within one and the same piece, as in the French *rondeau* (Eng.: *Round O*), precursor of the Classical rondo, in which the first strain — the *rondeau* proper — acts as a refrain, alternating with a number of episodes or *couplets*, which may be in contrasting keys. The overall structure will thus be ABA, or ABACA, as in François Couperin's *Le Petit-Rien* (Bk II, p.50), or ABACADA and so on, depending on the number of episodes the composer chooses to include.

Tempo Baroque keyboard music contains comparatively few tempo marks. In keyboard dances the tempo depends on the characteristics of the type to which the dance belongs: *Bourrée, Gavotte, Minuet*, etc. These are discussed, in each volume of this anthology, at the first occurrence of the type concerned. Here, it is worth noting that the character of the various dance types did not remain static but evolved throughout the Baroque period. The original dance became more and more elaborate until it was transformed into a highly sophisticated work of art. Compare, for example, an early 17th-century Saraband by William Lawes (Bk I, p.10) with the final stage in the development of the dance as exemplified in Bach's E minor Partita, BWV 830. Increased elaboration had to be accommodated within a slower tempo. This explains why 17th-century dances are often faster than their 18th-century counterparts. When playing an Allemande by Purcell, for example (e.g. Bk III, p.22), one will adopt a brisker tempo and a lighter touch than in an Allemande by Bach or Couperin.

Pieces without dance titles may, nonetheless, belong to or resemble a particular dance type, and their tempo can be judged accordingly. Thus Dandrieu's *L'Agréable* (Bk I, p.58) is a Gavotte, and Clarke's *A Farewell* (Bk III, p.34) has the character of a Saraband. In illustrative pieces, whether or not dance-like, the tempo will depend on the expressive character or 'affect' of the piece. This will normally be indicated by the title, as in Rameau's *La Boiteuse* (Bk II, p.53) which, but for its name — 'The Lame Woman' — might be mistaken for a Gigue.

Where Italian tempo marks are present, it should be borne in mind that they refer primarily to the character of the piece rather than to its tempo. Thus *Allegro* denotes 'cheerfully' or 'lively' rather than fast, and *Adagio* 'at ease' rather than slow. The clearly marked differences of tempo now indicated by these terms did not then apply: an Andante and an Allegro might be similar in tempo but quite different in mood.

Dynamics 17th- and 18th-century keyboard instruments — the harpsichord, clavichord, virginals and spinet — can be played expressively by employing rubato and subtle variations of touch. But, except for the clavichord, they have very limited dynamic capabilities compared with the piano. To compensate for this deficiency, expressive equivalents of dynamics tend to be built into Baroque keyboard music by the composer. A rise and fall in pitch often has the same emotional effect as a dynamic rise and fall; notes at both extremes of the range can have a climactic effect; a full texture creates a *forte*, and a thin texture a *piano*; and the gradual addition of harmony notes can build a *crescendo*, their reduction a *diminuendo*. The two-manual harpsichord adds the further possibility of large-scale structural dynamics: the lower manual can be treated as equivalent to *forte*, and the upper to *piano*, while a *mezzo forte* can be achieved by playing with one hand on the upper manual and the other on the lower.

When transferring harpsichord music to the piano, real dynamics can be used where only the suggestion of their effect was possible on the harpsichord. The possibilities of expressive dynamic inflection available on the piano should be used to the full. But broader dynamic contrasts should be used sparingly and only where clearly warranted in the music. In binary pieces, for example, many of which will have been conceived with a single-manual instrument in mind, variety is to be achieved mainly by varying the repeats rather than by introducing sharp dynamic contrasts. On the other hand, such contrasts are often effective in the case of pairs of dances that are to be played *alternativement* (alternately): Böhm's Rigaudon-Trio-Rigaudon (Bk III, p.26), for example, might be played, broadly speaking, *forte-piano-forte*. And the scheme ABACA in the *rondeau* — the alternating theme and episodes — might be played *f p f p f* (or a more sophisticated dynamic scheme might be adopted, depending on the character of the episodes).

Ornamentation Ornaments are an essential ingredient of Baroque keyboard music, adorning the melody in an expressive piece and adding rhythmic sparkle in a more lively one. To omit them altogether would be to rob the music of much of its charm and vitality. On the contrary, where few ornaments, or none at all, are present in the text, the contemporary player would have been expected to improvise them. However, it is often possible to be selective and flexible in one's approach to ornaments. And this attitude is always greatly preferable to being so deterred by the profuseness of the ornamentation, particularly in French music, as not to play the music at all. The recommended approach is to learn the music without the ornaments first, then add the essential ones — cadential shakes, and ornaments without which the melody sounds incomplete or impoverished — treating the remainder as optional, or reserving them for the repeats. Ornaments should be practised very slowly at first. Long shakes that enhance an expressive melody should be played with a certain rubato, a slight acceleration into the repercussions. Ornaments that add rhythmic life should be fast, crisp, even and accented.

Many different signs were used for one and the same ornament during the Baroque period. The original signs have been retained in this anthology — for it is important to grow accustomed to them — and an editorial explanation is given alongside them. As an aid to the elucidation of the signs, the tables of ornaments that many Baroque composers included in their keyboard publications are valuable as far as they go, but they do not show the many local variations of treatment that are necessary according to the specific context in which the ornament is placed. Here musical imagination and sensitiveness come into play, coupled with a respect for historical knowledge and accuracy. Many examples of a suggested variety of execution will be found in the course of this anthology. Here, a few more general points should be made.

The speed and number of repercussions of a shake will depend on the length of the note and the tempo. In the early 17th century, shakes more often begin on the main note; in the late 17th and

18th century, on the note above. But this decision, too, depends partly on context. Upper-note shakes (Ex. a) are, in effect, accented and appoggiatura-like. Where this effect is undesirable, as in the case of legato (b), fast tempo (c) or repeated notes (d), a main-note shake may be preferable.

Similarly on-the-beat ornaments are, in the mid and late Baroque, more common than before- and between-beat ornaments, but there is no doubt that in certain contexts the less usual alternatives are intended. Thus:

(a)   =   but (b)   =

The question where the accent falls is, again, crucial. In (a) the main note, and therefore also the appoggiatura that replaces it, is accented; in (b) neither is accented.

Touch In early keyboard music, unlike that of the 19th century, a *non legato* touch is best regarded as the norm, and *legato* as only one among several different possibilities. The type of touch required is not necessarily indicated by the composer. Thus might, more often than not, be played thus: ; but it could also be played *staccato* — , *staccatissimo* — , *legato* — , or *legatissimo* — .

The last-named type of touch — in effect, overlapping — is much more effective than plain legato in achieving a convincing *cantabile* on the harpsichord and can be usefully transferred to the piano. It is recommended by Rameau in the execution of appoggiaturas, in which it is essential to avoid any perceptible break between the grace-note and its resolution: (i.e.) = .

Articulation In executing a melodic line, a considerable variety of touch is desirable. By varying the touch, the player *articulates* the phrase; that is to say, joins some notes and separates others. Articulation is the most effective way of characterizing a piece in accordance with the intended 'affect' or expressive character. The decision whether to hold or release the keys, whether to join or separate the notes, will depend to a large extent on the accentuation of the passage concerned. Stressed notes should often be held or slurred, and unstressed notes shortened. And an accent is best achieved not by force but by shortening the previous note. Loeillet's Minuet in A (Bk III, p.58), for example, begins (omitting the ornaments):

In bb.1 & 3 the accent is on the 2nd beat of the bar; in bb.2 & 4 on the 1st beat. This can be clarified by the following articulation:

In the original, Loeillet's shakes and mordents further underline the accentuation.

Short slurred groups are, in Baroque music, far more common than long undifferentiated stretches of legato. In practice, a slurred pair or group of notes should be clearly set off from its surroundings by shortening the last note: thus ♪♩ = ♪♪♩ . The effect of a slur can be further marked by accenting the first note and then gradually reducing the tone. Appoggiaturas should invariably be played in this way, whether written out in full or notated as ornaments: thus ♪♩ = ♪♩ . The accent sign here indicates a slight increase in the velocity with which the finger strikes the key, not a muscular show of force. Applying these principles to Greene's Andante in A (Bk II, p.63), which, omitting a mordent on the 9th note, begins thus:

(the first crotchet in the 2nd bar forms a written-out appoggiatura), we arrive at:

Rhythm The notation of rhythm is often only approximate in Baroque music. The task of bringing it to life by imparting grace or vitality (depending on the context) to the notated rhythms is left in the hands of the performer. This often means employing various forms of rubato. One of the most common of these is *inequality* or *notes inégales:* the unequal playing of notes that are notated as equal in length. Typically, flowing quavers or semiquavers are played with a very slight long-short lilt; thus, very approximately, ♪♪♪♪♪♪ = ♪♪♪♪♪♪ . Since unequal playing is designed to enhance the grace and elegance of a melody, it is confined to mainly conjunct, melodic notes; largely disjunct or broken-chordal notes should remain equal. If notes are slurred in pairs — ♫ or ♫ — the inequality is reversed so that the notes are played in short-long groups (♫ or ♪♩): the so-called Scotch Snap or Lombardic rhythm. The degree of inequality adopted is a matter of taste, varying from one piece to another — it will clearly be more pronounced in vigorous pieces, less so in expressive ones — and even within a piece. *Notes inégales* belong primarily to French music but are by no means confined to it: they became common practice in England after the Restoration and should no doubt often be applied in German music written — as is frequently the case — in the French style.

A related convention is *the variable value of the dot*. Rhythms notated unequally may be, in practice, more or less unequal than written, depending on the intended effect. Thus ♩.♪ may either be played as written (perhaps modified to ♩·♪ in more vigorous passages) or softened to ♩♪ . And ♩.♪ may be sharpened to ♩··♪ or ♩·♪ . The increased vigour of sharpened dotted rhythms is useful not only in lively pieces but in slow ones, such as Sarabands, in which the rhythm would otherwise sound sluggish.

It is often necessary to *assimilate* variously notated rhythms to the prevailing rhythm of a piece. Thus in many cases *all* the rhythms of a piece should be dotted, despite the fact that only some of them are thus notated. Here are some examples of rhythmic assimilation:

(a)

(b)

(c)

In Ex. (a) the quaver rhythm of the 1st beat is assimilated to the dotted quaver rhythm of the 2nd. In (b) the dotted crotchet rhythm of the upper part falls in line with the dotted quaver rhythm of the lower. And in (c) the dotted rhythms of one part are adjusted to the triplet rhythms of the other.

One further rhythmic characteristic of Baroque music should be mentioned here briefly, namely *hemiola* rhythm. Triple-time pieces often include a pair of bars that are to be played as if they were notated as three bars of duple time. The passage must be articulated in such a way that the temporary change of metre is made absolutely clear. In this anthology, hemiola is shown by square brackets, as in this example from Fischer's Minuet in A minor (Bk III, p.28):

which should be played thus:

Harmony Due to the characteristics of Baroque keyboard instruments, chordal passages and harmonic accompaniments are normally broken into more or less elaborate patterns in order to fill the texture, enrich the harmonic background, and preserve interest and vitality. The term *style brisé*, or 'broken style', though strictly speaking referring to the transference of lute figuration to 17th-century French harpsichord music, is often extended to cover this characteristic of Baroque keyboard textures in general. Here is a simple example from Dieupart's Passepied in D (Bk II, p.29). The bass and harmony of bb.1–4 are standard:

but instead of notating the chords thus, Dieupart indicates that they are to be broken and their notes sustained for the length of the bar:

This kind of texture, in which notes are struck frequently and, being sustained, overlap with one another, is ideally suited to the keyboard. And harmony in Baroque keyboard music, however notated, tends to gravitate towards it.

Thus chords notated as unbroken should often be spread or *arpeggiated:*

   might be played   or

Various signs are used to indicate arpeggiation, the most familiar of which is   , but it is often left to the player to decide how and where to arpeggiate chords. More elaborate forms of arpeggiation are frequent and may either be indicated by signs, as in the last bar of each strain of Rameau's *Le Lardon* (Bk II, p.52), or notated in full, as in the last two bars of Purcell's Prelude in C, Z.665/1 (Bk III, p.22). Examples such as these provide models for more elaborate extempore arpeggiation elsewhere. Arpeggiated chords can, further, be embellished by incorporating slides (Ex. a) and passing acciaccaturas (Ex. b; non-harmonic notes that are not sustained):

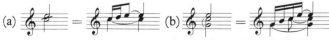

These ornaments would frequently have been added in performance, regardless of whether or not they were indicated by the composer.

Not only are chords notated as such often broken, but — conversely — the notes of broken-chordal figures are often sustained to build up chords. This may be indicated by slurs, as in bb.12 & 16 of Rameau's *La Boiteuse* (Bk II, p.53), or by double-stemming, as in the r.h. part of Dandrieu's *La Prévenante* (Bk II, p.54). But it is often left unnotated and has to be inferred from the character of the music. In *L'Amusante* (Bk III, p.56), Daquin assists the player by marking the l.h. quavers 'nottes très liées' ('notes very joined'):

should therefore be played thus:

Molto tenuto playing of this kind is a very common resource in harpsichord music and should be used in place of the sustaining pedal when Baroque keyboard music is transferred to the piano.

Fingering Our modern fingering methods have a tendency to encourage the continuous legato that is more appropriate to 19th-century keyboard music than to that of the Baroque period. To a certain extent, therefore, it is desirable to revive older fingering methods when playing the music of this period. Fingerings should be used that facilitate the possibilities on either side of legato: overlapping (as in *tenuto* and *legatissimo*) and separation (breaks between slurs and *non legato*). Changing fingers on held notes is particularly useful as a means of sustaining harmony notes, as in this example from Fischer's Minuet in F (Bk II, p.25):

Middle parts in a contrapuntal texture often have to be divided between the hands in order to maintain the same articulation at every occurrence of the theme — see, for example, the *Tastata* from Pasquini's Suite in G, bb.2–3 (Bk III, p.24). The use of the same finger on successive notes can force separation, either of single notes, as in Purcell's *Prelude for the fingering* (Bk I, p.21; see r.h., bb.8–14 and l.h., bb.5–6 and 10–13), which is fully fingered in the original, or of short phrases, as in Dieupart's Passepied in D (Bk II, p.29), bb.11–14:

Breaking a line into short slurred groups can be enforced by other forms of disjunct fingering, as in this example from Rameau's Minuet I in G (Bk III, p.53), bb.18–20 (treble only, ornaments omitted):

where the suggested fingering encourages the correct articulation of the suspension:

Placing long fingers over short (3 over 4; 3 or 4 over 5), as in

William Lawes's *Symphony*, bb.13–14 (Bk III, p.17), and lateral shifts of hand-position, as in Locke's Prelude in C, bb.15–16 (Bk II, p.16), are very useful older alternatives to thumb-under movements. The one method has the advantage that it turns the hand in the playing direction; the other, that it helps to maintain a quiescent hand.

Finally, avoid placing the short thumb and little finger on black notes wherever possible. And practice executing shakes and mordents on 4 3 and even 5 4, as well as on the more usual 3 2 and on alternate fingers.

EDITORIAL METHOD

Texts are based, for the most part, on the original editions, but occasionally on autographs (where extant) or early manuscript copies. The editorial aim has been to adhere as closely as possible to the composer's original text by transcribing directly from the best available sources and by keeping editorial alterations and additions to a minimum. Any editorial marks are, moreover, clearly differentiated as such. Suggestions for ornament realizations (at the first occurrence of a particular ornament in a specific context) and for phrasing and articulation, arpeggiation, and the application of rhythmic conventions are given either in words at the end of the piece or in small notation between the staves. Fingering, commas (showing breaks between phrases) and accidentals to ornaments are editorial unless otherwise stated. All other editorial marks are given in small print or square brackets, with the exception of words (italics; original words are roman), slurs and ties ( ), indications of hemiola or other rhythmic displacements ( ), allocation of notes to r.h. or l.h. (R/L or ⌐/⌐), and the reminder that a note, being present simultaneously in another part, should not be struck (round brackets).

ACKNOWLEDGEMENTS

Most grateful thanks are due to the music departments of the following libraries for granting access to, or providing microfilms of, the manuscripts and first editions in their possession and for permitting their use as the sources of this anthology: Deutscher Staatsbibliothek, Berlin; Staatsbibliothek Preussischer Kulturbesitz, Berlin; The Fitzwilliam Museum, Cambridge; Hessische Landes- und Hochschulbibliothek, Darmstadt; Musikbibliothek der Stadt Leipzig; The British Library, London; The Bodleian Library, Oxford; and the Bibliothèque Nationale, Paris.

RICHARD D. P. JONES
Oxford, 1988

Note to Book I

Though all the pieces in Book I have been chosen on the grounds that they qualify for the epithet 'easy', their technical demands inevitably vary. For if the contents had been levelled down too rigorously, they would have offered a diet of little other than minuets! The easiest pieces, such as those by Telemann and Handel, consist simply of treble and bass (the easiest of all being Rameau's *Menuet en Rondeau* in C). Pieces whose texture is essentially in three parts, such as the opening English group, the Blow Gavotte and Saraband, and Purcell's version of 'Lilliburlero' (*A new Irish Tune*), constitute an intermediate group. The hardest pieces are those which are clothed in the richest texture: the Frescobaldi, Chambonnières, Louis Couperin and Böhm. Since the composers named wrote nothing easier, to omit these pieces would be to exclude some of the key figures of the period.

Profusely ornamented pieces – six French (Lebègue, le Roux, Marchand, F. Couperin, Dandrieu and Daquin) and one English (John Barrett) – form a special group. They are relatively straightforward if played without ornaments but become appreciably harder when the ornaments are added. Accordingly, they are here given in two versions: an editorial plain version, in which all but the essential ornaments are omitted; and the composer's own ornamented version. Students are encouraged to start with the plain text but to advance to the ornamented one when they become more proficient at executing ornaments.

Saraband

William Lawes
(1602–1645)

William Lawes was younger brother of the composer Henry Lawes. He was a musician at the court of Charles I, served in the royalist army, and was killed in battle.

The *Saraband* is a triple-time dance of Latin American and Spanish origin. 17th-century Sarabands, like this one by Lawes, were often fairly fast and lively: quite different from the slow, solemn Sarabands of a later period.

Suggested phrasing: ♩ ♩ ♩ ♪ ♪ | ♩ ♩ ♪ | ♩ ♩ ♩ ♩ ♩ ♩ | ♩ ♪ ♪. :|| . Double-dot the rhythm ♩. ♪ to ♩.. ♪. The square brackets in the last two bars denote hemiola rhythm – from the middle of b.7 think in minim beats, ignoring the bar-line: ♩. ♪♪♪♪♪ ♪.

Source: *Musicks Hand-maide* (London, 1663). No time signature.

Saraband

Albertus Bryne
(c. 1621–1671)

Albertus Bryne was for many years organist of St Paul's Cathedral. Later he was John Blow's predecessor as organist at Westminster Abbey.

This piece has in common with the Lawes piece (No.1) the repeated-note figure that was typical of the early English Saraband. The feminine cadences are another common feature of the type.

The cadential ornaments (bb.2, 4 & 9) are essential, but the others could be treated as optional. Suggested phrasing: ♩ ♩ ♩ ♩. ♪♪|♫♫♫♪ ♩.
The syncopation in bb.5–6 should be played ♩ ♩ or, with the ornament, ♫♩ ♩ . Dotted crotchet rhythms might be sharpened to ♩.. ♪ .
The 3-bar phrase at the close, following a series of 2-bar phrases, creates an effective asymmetry.

Source: *Musicks Hand-maide* (London, 2nd edn, 1678). No time signature.

Duke of York's March

Anon.

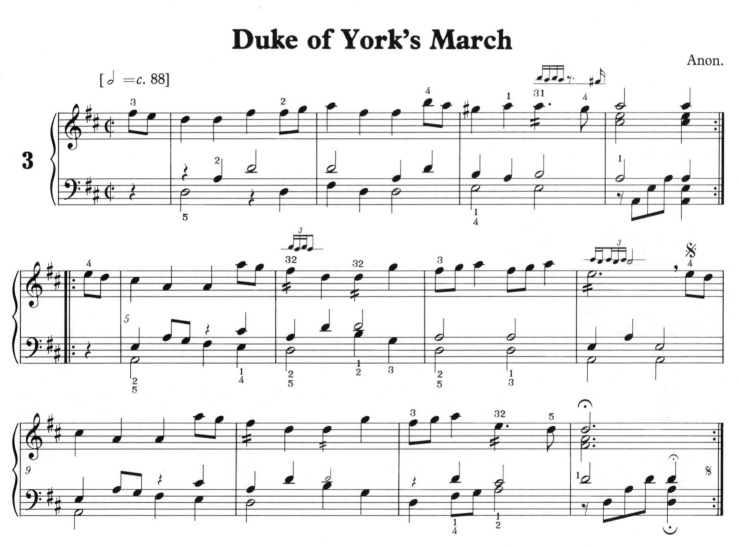

This is a quick march with two minim drum beats per bar. According to Thurston Dart, it is named after James Stuart, second son of Charles I, who became James II in 1685.

Suggested phrasing: ♫|♩ ♩ ♩ ♫|♩ ♩ ♩ ♫|♩ ♩ ♩. ♪♩ ♩; and in b.7: ♫♩ ♫♩. The sign 𝄋 at the end of b.8 indicates the *petite reprise*: the last four bars (plus upbeat) are to be played again at the end, after the second half as a whole has been repeated. The ornaments in bb.6, 8 & 10 could be omitted, but the cadential shakes in bb.3 & 11 are essential.

Source: *Musicks Hand-maide* (London, 1663). B.12, l.h., last chord: minims, and *D* not *d'*, but cf. b.4.

Ayre

Benjamin Rogers
(1614–1698)

[Lively ♩=c. 66]

Benjamin Rogers was, from 1665 to 1686, organist and choirmaster at Magdalen College, Oxford.

The term *Air* was often borrowed from vocal music to describe a short tuneful instrumental piece. The dotted rhythms in the first bar-and-a-half of Rogers' *Ayre* probably indicate how pairs of quavers are to be played throughout. Suggested phrasing of the 1st strain: ; and of the 2nd strain: . If the ornaments are omitted in the first two bars, use the 2nd finger in place of 32. The cadential ornaments are essential.

Source: *Musicks Hand-maide* (London, 1663).

The Simerons Dance

Matthew Locke
(*c.*1622–1677)

[Brisk ♩.=c. 72]

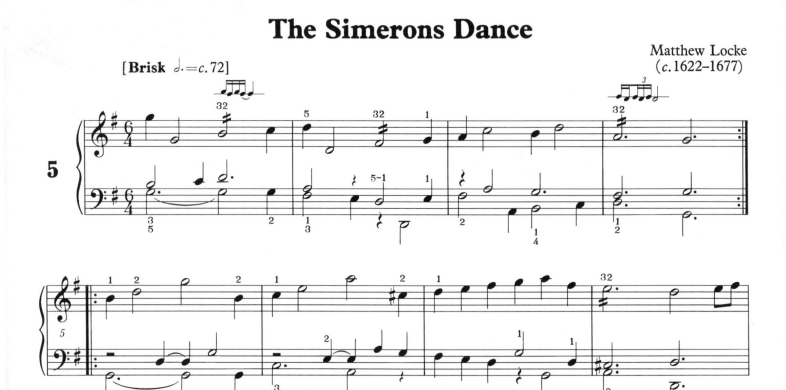

Matthew Locke was one of the most outstanding forerunners of Purcell. He trained as a chorister at Exeter Cathedral and became a court musician after the Restoration of 1660.

This piece is taken from Locke's incidental music to a play by Sir William D'Avenant entitled *The History of Sir Francis Drake* (1658). The 'Simerons', or Cimmerians, are the natives of Latin America, whose dance is thought to be comic and grotesque.

Mark the syncopation of the theme thus: ♩♩ ♩ ♩|♩♩ ♩ ♩ . In bb.5–6, the r.h. minims are imitated in the tenor part, which should be played as if in 3/2: ‒ ♩ ♩ | ‒ ♩ ♩♩ . The r.h. crotchets in b.7 might be phrased: ♩♩♩♩♩ . The piece is in rounded binary form, for the closing phrase (bb.9–12) forms an enhanced restatement of the first four bars.

Source: *Musicks Hand-maide* (London, 1663). Time signature: $\mathsf{C}\,\frac{3}{1}$

Allman

Matthew Locke

6

'Alman' is an Anglicized version of *Allemande* (French for 'German dance'), a dance in moderate four-time. 17th-century Allemandes were, in general, quicker and lighter than those of, say, Bach or Couperin: Thomas Mace, in *Musick's Monument* (1676), describes the dance as 'very Ayrey and Lively'.

This piece illustrates the imitative texture that became typical of the Allemande. The essential ornaments are the cadential ones in bb.5 (4th crotchet), 9 & 12; the others could be omitted. Spread all 3- or 4-note chords (the last chord of the piece might be spread downwards in the rhythm ♫♫♩).

Source: *Musicks Hand-maide* (London, 2nd edn, 1678). No time signature. The 1st-time bar, b.6a, is editorial. B.10, tenor, 5–6: tone too high; b.12, last tenor note: *e* not *g*.

Corrente prima

Girolamo Frescobaldi
(1583–1643)

7

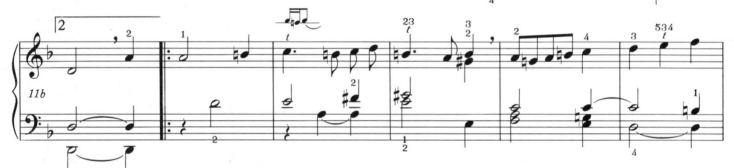

Frescobaldi was organist at St Peter's, Rome (1608–28 & 1634–43) and, for a shorter period (1628–34), at the Medici court in Florence. He was the most important Italian keyboard composer before Domenico Scarlatti.

The *Corrente* (literally 'running') is a fast dance in triple time: the Italian equivalent of the French *Courante*. The *Corrente Prima*, the first of four Correntes, contains no ornaments, but contemporary players would have been expected to improvise them. An optional scheme of ornaments is therefore provided here by the editor. Note that ornaments at this period often anticipate the beat, and shakes more often than not start on the main note.

Suggested phrasing (bb.1–6):

Source: *Il primo Libro d'Intavolatura di Toccate di Cimbalo et Organo* (Rome, 1628). Key signature: no flat; time signature: C3; final chord: semibreves. The 1st-time bars are editorial.

Sarabande

Jacques Champion de Chambonnières
(*c.* 1602–1672)

Chambonnières, harpsichordist to Louis XIII and Louis XIV, was founder of the French classical school of harpsichord playing and composition. He developed an idiomatic style based on the *style brisé* (broken or arpeggiated texture) of the French lutenists.

This Sarabande (Eng.: *Saraband*) illustrates the characteristic feminine cadences of the dance but lacks the 2nd-beat stresses that later became typical.

The ornaments are editorial, for there are none in the original. The cadential shakes are essential, but the remaining ornaments can be omitted or reserved for the repeats. Accelerate somewhat into the long shakes.

The chords should be spread, the dotted rhythms sharpened to ♩·· ♪ and the quavers of b.10 played unequally (see Introduction, p.7): . Phrasing will tend to stress the first beat of the bar; thus bb.7–8: . The sign ⅋ in b.13 announces the *petite reprise*: a final repeat of the last four bars after the 2nd half as a whole has been repeated.

Source: Bauyn MS. Upper stave: soprano clef. Time signature: 3. B.11, tenor, beats 2–3: tied minim *g*.

Branle de Basque

Louis Couperin
(c. 1626–1661)

9

ossia:

Louis Couperin, organist of St Gervais, Paris, was uncle of the more famous François Couperin and one of the most distinguished pupils of Chambonnières.

The *Branle de Basque* is one of many local varieties of the *Branle:* a popular Renaissance round dance. Play the quavers unequally (see Introduction, p.7): roughly ♩♪|♩ ♩♪ ; mark the syncopation in b.2 (and parallels) thus: ♩ ♩ ; and play upbeat crotchets staccato. Elsewhere r.h. crotchets might be slurred in pairs, e.g. b.3: ♩♩ ♩♩. Below the stave in bb.13–15 is an editorial alternative for players who cannot comfortably stretch a 10th.

Source: Bauyn MS. The title is crossed out, except for 'de Mr. Couperin'. B.8b is editorial. B.15, last treble note: *g″* not *f″*; b.16a, alto: ♩ ♩; tenor: ♪ ♩. ; bass: o .

Gavotte
Plain Version

Nicolas-Antoine Lebègue
(c. 1631–1702)

10a

Gavotte
Ornamented Version

Nicolas-Antoine Lebègue

[♩ =c. 104]

10b

Lebègue was a French composer who became *organiste du roi* (royal organist) in 1678 and was very influential as a teacher.

The *Gavotte* is a pastoral French dance in moderate 2/2 or ₵ time. Phrases usually begin and end half-way through a bar, and another version of this piece (from the Bauyn MS) is notated thus: ₵ ♫♫♫ | ♩. ♪♫♫♫ | ♩. ♪♫♫ | ♫♫♩. ♫ | ♩ ‖

This Gavotte was one of the most popular pieces in the entire literature of 17th-century French harpsichord music. It is given here in two versions: a plain version, in which all the ornaments, except the essential ones at the cadences, have been omitted by the editor; and the ornamented version of Lebègue's original edition.

Quavers should be played unequally throughout (see Introduction, p.7), not just those that are dotted: ♫ and ♫♪ both = roughly ♩ ♪ ; and ♩. ♪ = ♩ ♩ ♪ . 'R' in b.5 stands for *Reprise*, which indicates the beginning of the 2nd strain. The sign ⅗ in b.9 denotes the *petite reprise*: a final restatement of the last four bars after the 2nd strain as a whole has been repeated. Spread the 3-note r.h. chords, perhaps in the rhythm ♫♫♩ ; downwards in bb.4 & 12 and upwards in b.9.

Source: *Les Pièces de Clavessin* (Paris, 1677). 6th treble note of b.7: no sharp; 7th treble note of b.11: ꞈ (readings of this edition from the Bauyn MS).

AB 2085

Gavott

John Blow
(1649–1708)

11

John Blow, perhaps the most important of Purcell's English contemporaries, was a Gentleman of the Chapel Royal from 1674 and organist of Westminster Abbey from 1668. He relinquished the last-named post in 1679 to make way for his pupil Henry Purcell, but was reinstated after Purcell's death in 1695.

Suggested phrasing of the 1st strain: ♪♪ | ♩ ♪♪ ♩ | ♩ ♩ ♩ | ♩ ♪♪♪ | ♪♪♪♩ and of the 2nd strain: ♩ | ♩ ♪♪ ♩ ♩ | ♩ ♪♪ ♪♪ | etc. The cadential shakes in bb.8 & 12 are essential, but the other ornaments could be omitted by inexperienced players.

Source: *The Second Part of Musick's Hand-maid* (London, 1689). The 1st-time bars are editorial. A slightly more elaborate version (from which the title is taken) was published in Blow's *A Choice Collection of Lessons* (London, 1698).

Saraband

John Blow

12

Blow thought well enough of this piece to include it in his definitive published collection of harpsichord music (*A Choice Collection of Lessons*, London, 1698). As Howard Ferguson has shown, the version printed there spells out the correct interpretation of the rhythms: ♩. ♪ is to be played ♩. ♫; ♫ as ♫.; and ♫ (unslurred) as ♩ ♩ (perhaps softened in effect to ♩ ♪). Suggested phrasing (bb.1–4): ♩ ♩ ♩ | ♩.. ♪ | ♩ ♫ ♫. | ♪ ♩ . Of the ornaments, the mordents or *beats* (𝄿) are inessential, but the cadential shakes (≈) are obligatory. Note that the tempo is considerably quicker than that of a Saraband by Bach or Handel.

Source: *The Second Part of Musick's Hand-maid* (London, 1689). Time signature: 𝄴/31 . Tenor note in b.15: *d'* not *c'*. The version of the 1698 edition is somewhat more elaborate.

Air

John Blow

This finely shaped melody might be phrased thus: ♩ ♩ ♩ ♩ ♫ | ♫ ♫ ♩ ♩ | etc. The ornaments could be omitted by inexperienced players.

Source: London, British Library, Add. MS 22099. The notes in small print in b.8 appear to be later interpolations in the MS.

Prelude
Z.660/1

Henry Purcell
(1659–1695)

[**Moderate** ♩=c. 54]

14

Purcell ranks alongside William Byrd as one of the greatest of all English composers. In 1679, at the age of only 20, he succeeded his teacher John Blow as organist of Westminster Abbey. Like Mozart and Schubert, he died, tragically, when still only in his thirties.

The *Prelude*, the earliest type of pure keyboard music, was originally improvised. Preludes are often built out of figurations idiomatic to the keyboard: in this case, broken chords. Play with a *legato* or *legatissimo* touch. Note how both r.h. and l.h. figures are inverted in the 2nd half of the piece, starting half-way through b.5.

Source: *A Choice Collection of Lessons for the Harpsichord or Spinnet* (London, 1696).

Minuet
Z.649

Henry Purcell

[♩=c. 144]

15

Fine

End with the first Strain

A *Round O* (Fr.: *rondeau*) with a single episode (bb.9–12), so that the structure is ABA. Concerning the Minuet as a dance-type, see under le Roux's *Menuet* (p.27). Suggested phrasing: ♫♫♩ | ♩ ♩ ♩ | ♩ ♩ ♩ | ♩ ♩ etc. Play slurred quaver pairs – ♫ – as Scotch snaps: ♫.

Source: *The Second Part of Musick's Hand-maid* (London, 1689). Time signature: $\frac{C}{31}$. The 1st time bar – b.8a – is editorial. Pause to last treble note (b.12).

Prelude for the fingering

Henry Purcell

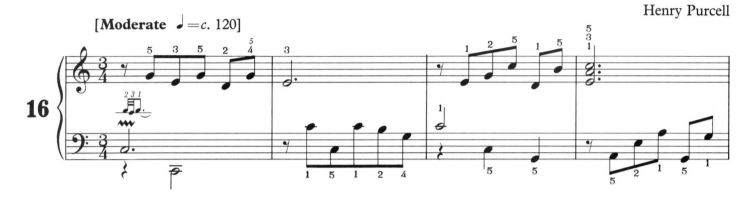

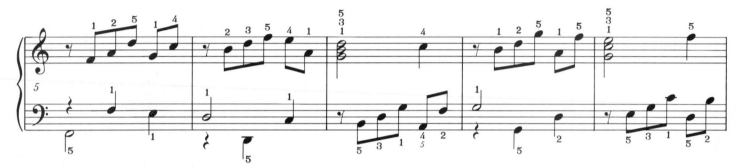

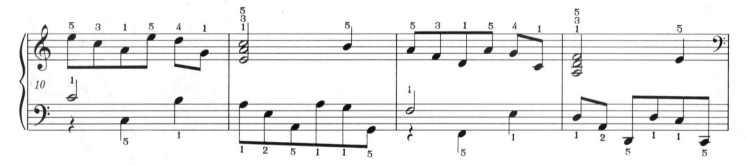

This piece, like the same composer's Prelude in G, Z.660/1 (see p.20), is built out of idiomatic broken-chordal figurations. Chords notated as *unbroken*, as in the r.h. of b.4, should nonetheless be spread.

Purcell's own fingering is given here (a few editorial alternatives are printed in italics). Note how the use of the little finger of the r.h. (bb.8–14) or the thumb of the l.h. (bb.10–14) on consecutive notes forces detached playing. The elaborate written-out arpeggiation in the second-last bar may serve as a model for extempore arpeggiation elsewhere. Complete the pattern by spreading the final chord quickly upwards.

Source: *The Harpsichord Master* (London, 1697). Time signature: 3. The l.h. is fingered 1–5 from little finger to thumb. The piece is not listed in Zimmerman's catalogue of Purcell's works.

Jig
Z.T686

Henry Purcell

17

This Jig and the Hornpipe that follows are keyboard transcriptions from Purcell's incidental music to *Abdelazer, or the Moor's Revenge*, a tragedy by Aphra Behn.

The English *Jig*, forerunner of the French *Gigue*, is in a lively 6/8 with dotted rhythms. Suggested phrasing: ♪ | ♩ ♪ ♪ | ♩ ♩ ♪♫♪ | ♫ ♫ ♫ ♫ | ♩. ♩. Omit the ornaments at first, but add them as soon as possible, for they add life and sparkle to the music. Spread the chords in bb.4, 8 & 12.

Source: *A Choice Collection of Lessons* (London, 1696). Time signature: 6/4.

Hornpipe
Z.T683

Henry Purcell

18

AB 2085

The *Hornpipe* is a lively English dance in quick triple time. Suggested phrasing: ♪♫♫ ♫ etc. The ornaments are essential.

Source: London, British Library, Add. MS 22099. No time signature.

Song Tune

Z.T694

Henry Purcell

[**Moderate** ♩=c. 144]

19

A keyboard version of the song 'Ah how pleasant 'tis to love', Z.353. Suggested phrasing: ♩ ♩|♩ ♩ |♩ ♩|♩. |♩. ♪♪|♩♩♩♩|♩. ♪♪|♩. .
Play slurred quaver pairs – ♫ – as Scotch snaps: ♫. .

Source: *The Second Part of Musick's Hand-maid* (London, 1689). Time signature: 31.

A new Irish Tune

Z.646

Henry Purcell

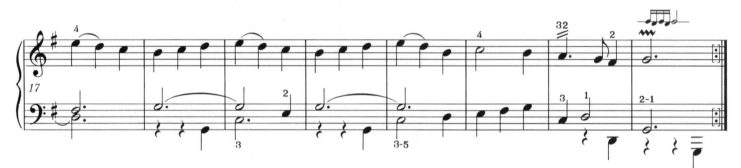

This is Purcell's arrangement of the famous anonymous tune *Lilliburlero*, which had first appeared in print only a few years before, hence the 'new' of the title.

Sharpen the rhythm ♩. ♪ to ♩.. ♪ and play slurred pairs of crotchets as Scotch snaps (♪♩. or ♪♩..). Suggested phrasing: ♩. ♪♩ | ♩ ♩ | ♩. ♪♩ | ♩. | ♩ ♩ ♩ | ♩ | ♩. ♪♩ | ♩. . The *forefall* (rising appoggiatura) in b.11 has to be played before the beat to avoid parallel 5ths with the bass.

Source: *The Second Part of Musick's Hand-maid* (London, 1689). Time signature: 2/3.

Three Arias

Bernardo Pasquini
(1637–1710)

2 [**Allegro moderato** ♩ =*c*. 88]

3 [**Vivace** ♩. =*c*. 76]

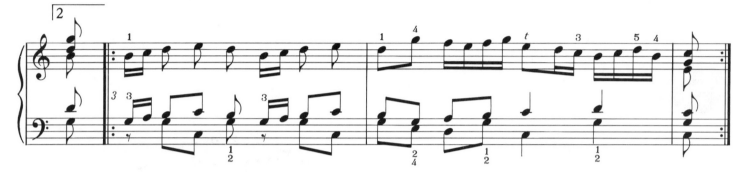

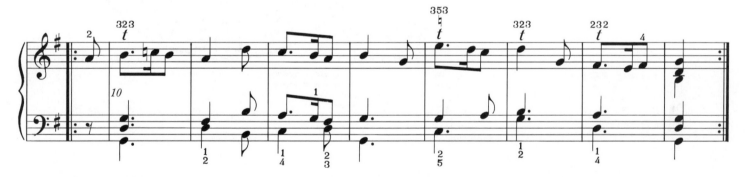

Bernardo Pasquini, organist of S. Maria in Aracoeli from 1664, was renowned as a keyboard virtuoso. He was the outstanding Italian keyboard composer between Frescobaldi and Domenico Scarlatti.

The term *Aria*, like *Air*, was borrowed from vocal music to describe a short tuneful instrumental piece. Of the three Arias given here, the second has become familiar in Respighi's adaptation as the prelude to his orchestral suite *gli Uccelli* (The Birds; 1927).

Suggested phrasing of No.1: ⁊ ♪♪♪♪ ♫ ♫♫ | ♫ ♪·♫ ; and of No.2: ⁊ ♫♫♫ ♫♫♫ | ♫ ♫♫ ♫♫ ♫♫ | ♪ . No.3 is one-in-a-bar, with staccato upbeat quavers; lean on the strong beats thus: ♩· ♫ .

Source: London, British Library, Add. MS 31501, Vol. III (autograph). Nos.1 & 2 are entitled 'Aria'; No.3 is unnamed. Upper stave: soprano clef. The 1st-time bar in No.2 is editorial. Key signature in No.3: no sharp.

Aria

Bernardo Pasquini

A study in the typical Baroque keyboard texture in which a short scalic motif is repeatedly passed from one hand to the other. Use mixed phrasing in the quavers, e.g. ♪♪♪♪♪ , and spread the accompanying chords lightly.

Source: London, British Library, Add. MS 31501, Vol.III (autograph). No title. Upper stave: soprano clef.

Menuet

Plain Version

Gaspard le Roux
(c. 1660–c. 1706)

Menuet

Ornamented Version

Gaspard le Roux

23b

Reprise

Gaspard le Roux, one of the leading French harpsichordists of his day, published a single collection of suites in 1705. Most of the pieces therein are given in two versions: as harpsichord pieces and as instrumental trios.

The *Minuet* (French: *Menuet*), a dance in moderate triple time, originated as a French country dance and was introduced to the court of Louis XIV in the mid 17th century.

The plain version of le Roux's Minuet is editorial, omitting all but the essential ornaments; the ornamented version is that of the original edition.

Phrasing should emphasize the syncopation in alternate bars: ♩ ♩ | ♫♫♩ | ♩ ♩ | ♫♫♫ | etc. The unresolved dissonances in the l.h. (b.3 etc.) are deliberate, creating a rich harmonic background. Spread the r.h. chords in bb.8 & 16, perhaps downwards in the rhythm ♫♫♩ (b.8) or ♫♩ (b.16). Quavers should throughout be accorded the slight long-short lilt of *notes inégales* (see Introduction, p.7): thus ♫♫♫ = roughly ♩♪♩♪ . 'Reprise' in b.9 announces the 2nd strain.

Source: *Pièces de clavecin* (Paris, 1705). Time signature: 3. The piece is printed in parallel text with the trio version. It is followed by a 'Double du Menuet' and a 'Double de la Basse'.

Menuet [en] Rondeau

Plain Version

Louis Marchand
(1669–1732)

Louis Marchand was precocious as a child: he was appointed organist of Nevers Cathedral at the age of only 14. As an adult, he was much admired in his own country, France, as an organ virtuoso. He toured Germany from 1713 to 1717 and – so the story goes – failed to appear in a planned organ-playing contest with J. S. Bach in Dresden.

This Minuet illustrates, in a simple way, one of the most common French Baroque forms: the *rondeau*, in which a refrain – the *rondeau* proper – alternates with episodes or *couplets*. Marchand's Minuet has a single episode (bb.9–16), so that the structure is ABA. The return of the rondeau theme, normally indicated by a da capo, is here notated in full (bb.17–24).

Menuet [en] Rondeau

Ornamented Version

Louis Marchand

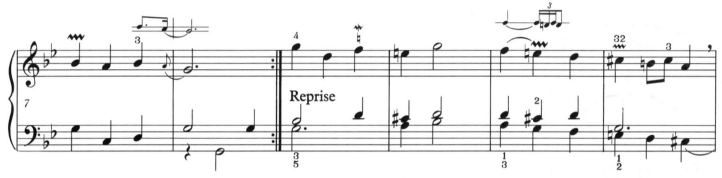

In the plain version, all the ornaments have been omitted by the editor. The ornamented version follows the original edition. Suggested phrasing: ♩♩♩|♩♩ |♩♩♩|♫♫♫ . Play the quavers in unequal pairs (see Introduction, p.7): roughly ♩♪ .

Source: *Pièces de Clavecin, Livre Second* (Paris, 1703). Key signature: one flat; time signature: 3.

The Prince of Denmark's March

Jeremiah Clarke
(c. 1674–1707)

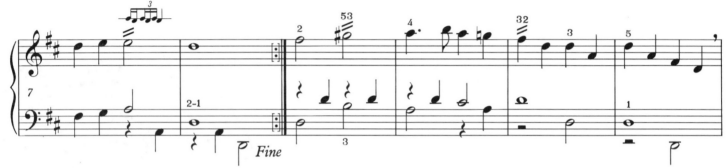

Clarke, one of Purcell's outstanding contemporaries, was a Gentleman of the Chapel Royal and organist – later also master of the choristers – at St Paul's Cathedral.

This famous piece was formerly known as 'Purcell's Trumpet Voluntary'. Apart from the false attribution to Purcell, that title was apt, for the treble part imitates the bright clear tones of the trumpet. In bb.17 ff., imagine a slow accompanying drum beat.

Round O is the Anglicized version of the French term *rondeau*: the structure is ABACA, the initial rondeau theme (bb.1–8) being repeated after each of the episodes (bb.9–16 & 17–24). Suggested phrasing of the opening theme: ♩ ♩ | ♩. ♪♪ ♩ | ♩ ♩ ♩ ♩ | ♩ ♩ ♩ ♩ ; of bb.11–12: ♩ ♩ ♩ ♩ | ♩ ♩ ♩ ♩ ; and of bb.17 ff.: ♩ ♫♩ ♩ etc.

Sources: *The Second Book of the Harpsichord Master* (London, 1700); *A Choice Collection of Ayres for the Harpsichord or Spinett* (London, 1700).

Aire

Jeremiah Clarke

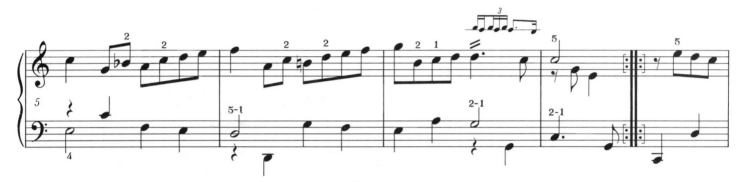

The first half of this finely-shaped melody is based on a rising 4-note scale; the second half, on its inversion.

Suggested phrasing (bb.1–4): ♩ ♫ | ♩ ♩ ♩ ♫ | ♩ ♩ ♪ ♫ | ♩ ♩ ♩ ♫ | ♩ ♩. Point the theme by making a clear break before the last three quavers of the bar in, for example, bb.5 & 6. The cadential shakes in bb.7, 11 & 15 are essential; the others, not so.

Source: *The Second Book of the Harpsichord Master* (London, 1700). No time signature. 3rd treble note of b.6: *d″* not *c″*, but cf. the previous sequential step. B.16a, bass: ♩ ♩ not ♩. ♪, but cf. b.8. The 2nd-time bar, b.16b, is editorial.

The Pilgrim

Plain Version

John Barrett
(*c.* 1676– *c.* 1719)

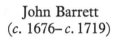

27a

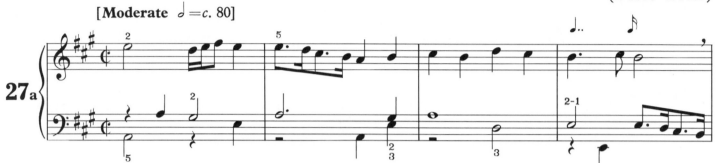

Fine

end with first part

John Barrett was a pupil of Blow's who became music master at Christ's Hospital, London and organist of St Mary-at-Hill.

The Pilgrim is a *Round O* (French: *rondeau*) with a single episode (bb.9–16), so that the structure is ABA. In the plain version, all the ornaments but one have been omitted by the editor; the ornamented version is Barrett's own.

AB 2085

The Pilgrim

Ornamented Version

John Barrett

end with first part

Suggested phrasing of the theme: ♩ ♫ ♩ | ♩. ♫. ♩ ♩ | ♩ ♩ ♩ ♩ | ♩. ; and of the episode: ♩ ♩ ♫ ♩ | ♩ ♩ ♩ ♩ | ♩ ♩ ♩ ♩ | 𝅝. The figure ♫ in bb.1, 9 & 14 is a written-out slide, which might be interpreted thus: ♫. The dotted rhythms should perhaps be softened to ♩ ♫ ♩.

Source: *The Third Book of the Harpsichord Master* (London, 1702). In a number of cases, a *forefall* ( ) is given where a *backfall* ( ) is required by the context. These have here been corrected by the editor without special notice.

Scotch Tune

William Croft
(1678–1727)

28

William Croft was a chorister, and later organist, at the Chapel Royal. In 1708 he succeeded his teacher John Blow as organist of Westminster Abbey.

This piece is a *Round O* (French: *rondeau*) with a single episode (bb.5–8), so that the structure is ABA. The opening might be phrased thus: ; and bb.6–7: etc.

Source: *The Third Book of the Harpsichord Master* (London, 1702). The 2nd-time bar, b.4b, is editorial. B.8, bass, 4th crotchet: *F* sharp not *D*.

Minuet

William Croft

29

This Minuet demands graceful phrasing: ♩♩♩ | ♩♩ ♩ | ♩ ♪. ♪. ♪ | ♩ ♪♪ . In the 2nd strain, clearly separate the steps of the sequence by falling 3rds: ♩ ♪♪ ♩ | ♩♩ ♪' | ♩ ♪♪ ♩ | ♩♩ etc. The square brackets in bb.14–15 denote hemiola rhythm – play as if in a temporary 2/4: ♩ ♩ | ♩ ♪♪ ♩ .

Source: *The Third Book of the Harpsichord Master* (London, 1702). No time signature.

Sarabande

Georg Böhm
(1661–1733)

30

The Lüneburg organist Georg Böhm was one of the most important German composers of the generation immediately before that of J. S. Bach. Bach, according to his son Carl Philipp Emanuel, 'loved and studied the works of Böhm'.

This piece belongs to the older type of Saraband (French: *Sarabande*), which was relatively quick in tempo. The pulse here is one-in-a-bar. One can imagine people dancing to this piece, whereas the later Bach Saraband is, by comparison, disembodied and idealized.

Spread the chords, and phrase the dotted rhythms thus: ♩. ♪♩ or (for example, in bb.22–3) ♩. ♪♩ . A contemporary player might have added shakes in bb.17, 19 & 22 thus: ♩. (= ♪♪♪♩).

Source: Berlin (West), Staatsbibliothek Preussischer Kulturbesitz, Mus. ms. 40644 (Möller MS). 1st alto note of b.22: minim dotted.

Sarabande

Johann Mattheson
(1681–1764)

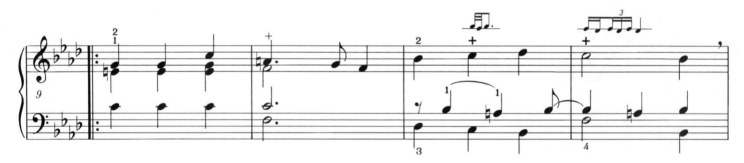

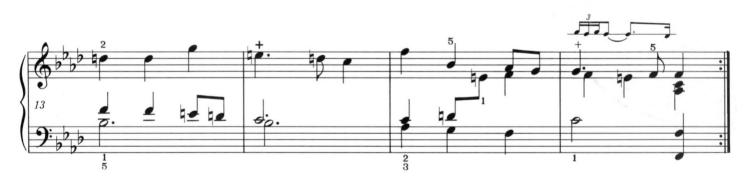

Johann Mattheson was, from 1715 to 1728, director of music at Hamburg Cathedral. A friend of Handel's, he was a fine organist and a prolific writer on music as well as a composer.

As a Saraband (Fr.: *Sarabande*), this piece lies somewhere between the light and simple dance of the earlier type (see, for example, Böhm's Sarabande on p.35) and the elaborate slow movement of Bach's maturity. Crotchet chords should be slightly detached and dotted crotchet rhythms sharpened to ♩.. ♪ or ♩. ♪ (except in the tenor part of b.7).

Source: *Pièces de Clavecin* (London, 1714). 4th movt of Suite No.12 in F min.; followed by 3 *doubles*. Key signature: 3 flats; time signature: 3.

Menuet

Johann Christoph Graupner
(1683–1760)

Graupner was, throughout most of his working life, Capellmeister (i.e. director of music) at the court of Darmstadt. Like his friend Telemann, he was an extremely prolific composer. But very little of his music is widely known (or even available) today, despite its attractiveness.

This piece takes the form of a *Menuet en rondeau* with a single episode (bb.17–32), so that the structure is ABA. Suggested phrasing (bb.1–4):

Source: Darmstadt, Hessische Landes- und Hochschulbibliothek, Mus. ms. 1231. Upper stave: soprano clef. Time signature: 3.

Aria

Georg Philipp Telemann
(1681–1767)

Telemann was, from 1721 until his death, director of music at the five principal churches in Hamburg and Cantor at the Johanneum. An extremely prolific composer, he was among the most important of Bach's German contemporaries.

The title 'Aria' is particularly apt in view of the *cantabile* character of this beautifully balanced melody. The figure ♪♫ in bb.1–2 etc. is a written-out appoggiatura. Play it thus: ♪ ♫, leaning on the note marked with an accent by dropping the wrist, and raising it on the note that follows. Mark the syncopation at the middle of b.12 and the beginning of b.13 by articulating the passage thus: ♫ ♫♫ etc.

Source: *Der getreue Music:Meister* (Hamburg, 1728). Upper stave: soprano clef.

AB 2085

Minue[tto]

Georg Philipp Telemann

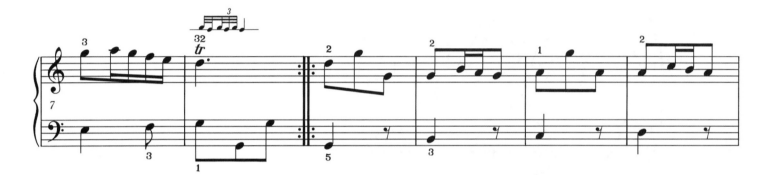

The third dozen of Telemann's Fantasias, from which this piece is taken, are deliberately written in the Italian style, as a foil to the second dozen, which are in the French style. Suggested phrasing of the theme: ♪♪♪♪ | ♪♪♪ etc.; and of the 2nd half: ♪♪♪ | ♪♪♪ etc.

Source: *Fantaisies pour le Clavessin* (Hamburg, 1732/3).

Gigue à l'Angloise

Georg Philipp Telemann

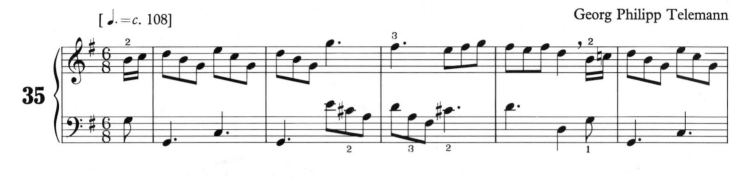

The title means 'Gigue in the English Style'. The 3-quaver groups can be phrased ♪♪♪ or ♪♪♪.

Source: *Der getreue Music:Meister* (Hamburg, 1728). Upper stave: soprano clef.

Dolce [in D minor]

Georg Philipp Telemann

This piece, like the Minuet in C (p.39), is taken from the third dozen of Telemann's Fantasias, which were deliberately composed in the Italian style.

The staccato wedges are equivalent to present-day staccato dots. By extension, perhaps all upbeat quavers should be staccato. Suggested phrasing of bb.1–2: ♪ | ♫♫♫ | ♫♫♫♫ ; b.5: ♪ | ♫♫♫ ♫♫♫ etc.; and bb.7–8: ♫ | ♫♫♫♫ | ♫♫♫ . Lean expressively on the written-out appoggiaturas (marked with an accent).

Source: *Fantaisies pour le Clavessin* (Hamburg, 1732/3).

Dolce [in G]

Georg Philipp Telemann

The first dozen of Telemann's three dozen Fantasias, from which this piece is taken, were deliberately composed in the Italian manner. The static harmony, the doubling of the treble in 3rds, and the written-out appoggiaturas give a foretaste – like much of Bach's keyboard music from around the same time – of pre-Classical style.

Adopt graceful mixed phrasing, leaning strongly on the appoggiaturas (marked with an accent in this example): ♫ ♩ ♩ | ♩ ♩ 𝄽 etc. Both ornaments are editorial; that of b.8 is optional, but the cadential shake in the second-last bar is essential.

Source: *Fantaisies pour le Clavessin* (Hamburg, 1732/3).

Menuet

HWV 450/6

George Frideric Handel
(1685–1759)

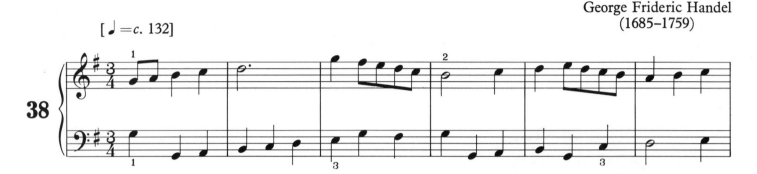

38

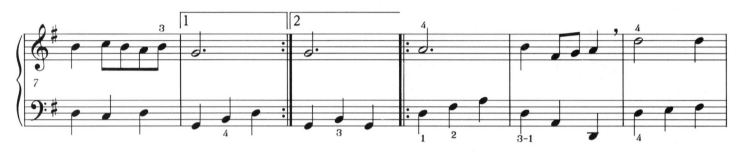

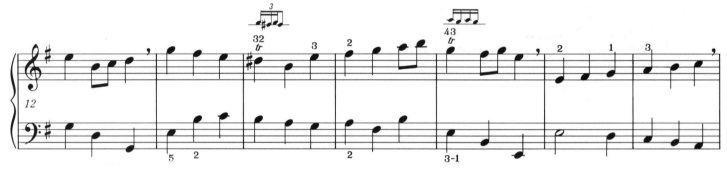

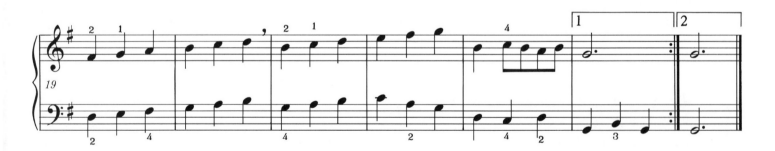

Handel's keyboard music is of minor importance compared with his operas and oratorios, but it is of consistently high quality and includes a great deal of attractive music. This Minuet is taken from a Partita in G which probably belongs to Handel's earliest period of composition and may have been written while he was still in his teens.

Suggested phrasing of the 1st half: ♩♩ ♩ | ♩. | ♩♩♩♩♩ | ♩ ♩ etc. and of the 2nd half: ♩. | ♩♩♩ etc. Bars of equal crotchets (e.g. bb.17 ff.) might be phrased thus: ♩ ♩ ♩ . The optional ornaments are editorial.

Source: Berlin (West), Staatsbibliothek Preussischer Kulturbesitz, Mus. ms. 9164/1 (MS copy). Upper stave: soprano clef. Bb. 8a & 24b are editorial (in b.24 the 2nd time is shown in the source by a pause to the 1st bass note).

Gavotte

HWV 491

George Frideric Handel

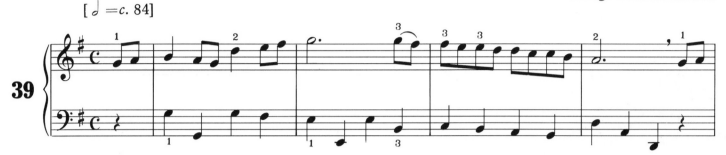

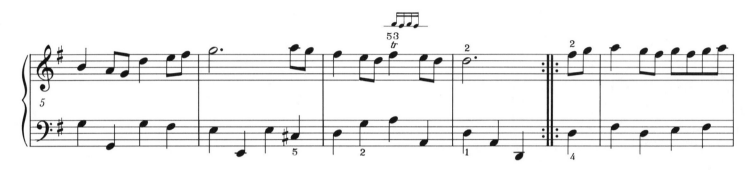

Like the Minuet that precedes it, this Gavotte probably belongs to Handel's earliest period of composition. Despite the title, which may not be Handel's, the rhythm of the piece is that of a Bourrée rather than a Gavotte. The time signature is also dubious: think in ₵ or 2/2 rather than in C.

Suggested phrasing (bb.1–4): ♪♪ | ♩ ♩♩ ♪♪ | ♩. ♪♪ | ♪♪♪♪ ♪♪♪♪ | ♩. . Thus, staccato quavers are answered by legato ones. Elsewhere (bb.9 & 11), groups of four quavers can be played ♪♪♪♪ . The optional ornaments are editorial.

Source: London, British Library, R.M. 19.a.4. (MS copy). Title: 'Gavotto'.

Impertinence

HWV 494

George Frideric Handel

40

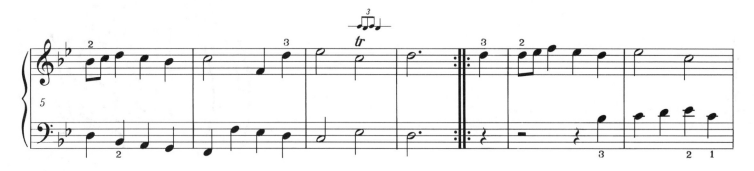

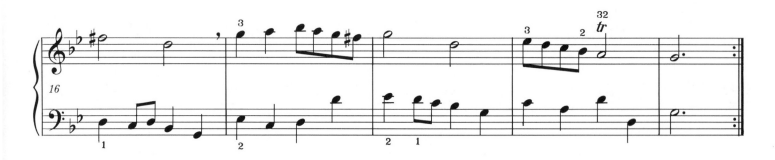

This early piece (*c.* 1705), in the style of a Bourrée, is conceived as a character-piece with a fanciful title.

Suggested phrasing (bb.1–4): ♩ ♩ ♩ ♩ ♫ | ♩ ♩ | ♫ ♩ ♩ | ♩ ♩ . The free imitation in the l.h. implies that similar phrasing should be used in both hands.

Source: London, British Library, R.M. 18.b.8. (MS copy).

[Sonatina]

HWV 582

George Frideric Handel

41

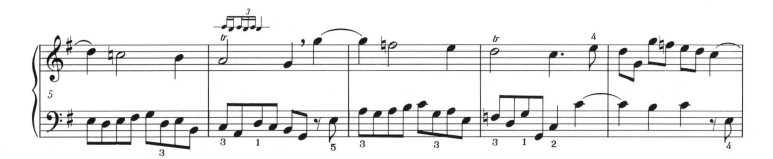

This piece represents the more mature Handel, for it was written in about 1722, probably for teaching purposes. It is conceived as a contrapuntal texture of two equal parts. The l.h. should therefore be no less prominent than the r.h.

Phrasing will be predominantly legato, but separate the first two beats of bb.1 & 3, l.h. and of b.2, r.h. in order to mark the syncopated minim: ♩ ♩ ♩ . The theme of b.1, r.h. is imitated at the 8ve below in b.2, l.h. In the r.h. of b.8, two phrases are dovetailed: the note c″ is at once the last note of a phrase and the first note of the restated theme in the subdominant key.

All the ornaments are editorial. The final cadential shake is essential, but the other ornaments are optional.

Sources: Cambridge, Fitzwilliam Museum, MS 263 (30.H.13.), p.5 (autograph); London, British Library, R.M. 18.b.8. (MS copy). The piece is unnamed in the autograph and entitled 'Fuga' in the copy. 7th bass note of b.5: *g* not *e*, but cf. bb.7 & 16.

AB 2085

Menuet *I*

Christian Petzold
(1677–1733)

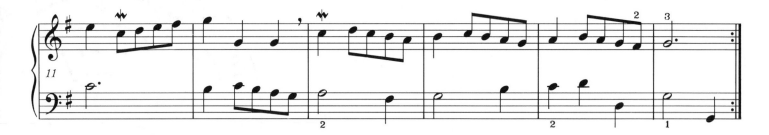

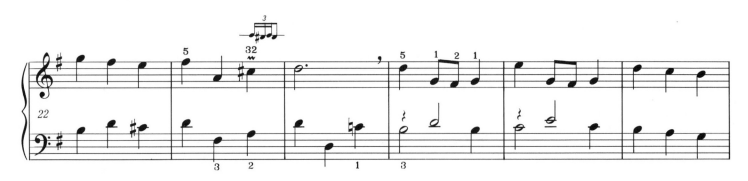

Menuet *II*

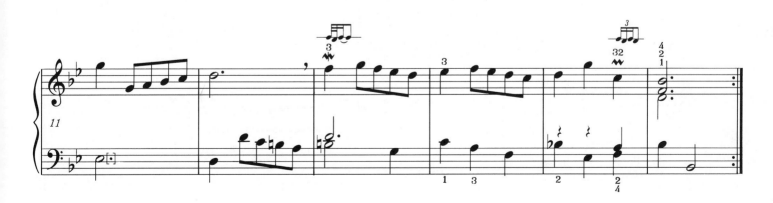

This famous pair of Minuets, formerly attributed to J. S. Bach, are now known to have been composed by the Dresden court organist Christian Petzold. Petzold's friendship with Bach is testified by the fact that, in 1727, he sold copies of Bach's 2nd & 3rd keyboard Partitas for him on commission. Bach's wife Anna Magdalena copied Petzold's Minuets into the *Clavierbüchlein* (Little Keyboard Book) that Bach dedicated to her in 1725.

Minuet II, in the tonic minor, is thematically related to Minuet I. The two pieces are designed to be played *alternativement*: that is to say, they are played one after the other without a break, Minuet I being played again (without repeats) after Minuet II. Suggested phrasing of Minuet I: ♩ ♪♪♪♪ | ♩ ♩ ♩ etc.; and of Minuet II: ♩ ♩ ♩ | ♩ ♩ ♩ | ♩ ♪♪♪♪ | 𝅗𝅥. . Groups of three crotchets can usually be phrased ♩ ♩ ♩ .

Source: Berlin (West), Staatsbibliothek Preussischer Kulturbesitz, Mus. ms. Bach P 225 (*Clavierbüchlein* for Anna Magdalena Bach, 1725). Upper stave: soprano clef. Time signature: 3. Key signature of Minuet II: one flat. Min. I, b.8, 2nd bass note: *C* not *d*. Min. II, b.27, last treble note: *c''* not *b'* flat; b.31, 1st treble note: 𝆖 not 𝆘. The Minuets are numbered BWV Anh.114 & 115 in Schmieder's catalogue. Concerning Petzold's authorship, see Schulze in *Bach-Jahrbuch*, 1979.

Sarabande

BWV 833/4

Johann Sebastian Bach
(1685–1750)

Bach's works for harpsichord and clavichord are the greatest achievements of the Baroque era in the sphere of keyboard music. The four pieces included in this volume are all taken from early works, which are often less elaborate and easier to play than the mature masterpieces.

This Sarabande belongs to one of Bach's earliest surviving keyboard compositions: the *Praeludium et Partita del Tuono Terzo* (i.e. in F. Major), BWV 833.

Within the 2-bar phrases, play the treble part in a *legato cantabile* style. The cadential shakes (bb.4, 8 & 12) are essential, but the ornaments in b.2 may be omitted by inexperienced players.

Source: Berlin (West), Staatsbibliothek Preussischer Kulturbesitz, Mus. ms. 40644 (Möller MS).

[Menuet and Trio]

BWV 820/3–4

Johann Sebastian Bach

TRIO

Menuet D.C.

The Menuet & Trio, like the Bourrée and Gigue that follow, belong to an early work: the *Ouverture* (i.e. suite) in F, BWV 820. They are designed to be played *alternativement*: the Minuet should be played again (without repeats) after the Trio, creating an overall ABA structure.

The Minuet is remarkable for its 3-bar phrases – a characteristic of some of the earliest examples of the dance type. Suggested phrasing (bb.1–3): ♩ ♩ | ♫ ♩. ♪ | ♩ ♩ . The square brackets in bb.16–17 denote hemiola – play as if in 2/4: ♩. ♪ | ♫♫ ♩ | ♩. ♪ . The cadential shakes are essential.

The Trio is designed as a simple rondeau (ABA), the opening theme recurring at b.17. Clearly articulated 2-bar phrases contrast with the 3-bar phrases of the Minuet. Suggested phrasing: ♩ ♫♩ | ♩. . In general, r.h. quavers might be largely legato as a foil to the detached quavers of the l.h. The walking bass of this l.h. part is very characteristic of Baroque music.

Source: Musikbibliothek der Stadt Leipzig, Ms. III. 8.4. (Andreas Bach Book). Time signatures: 3. All the 2nd-time bars are editorial.

Bourrée

BWV 820/5

Johann Sebastian Bach

[♩ =c. 100]

45

The *Bourrée* is a lively French dance in duple time (think in ¢ not C) with a crotchet upbeat. Despite its early date, this piece is characteristic, clearly foreshadowing the tuneful Bourrées of the English Suites and the Cello Suites.

Suggested phrasing (bb.1–4): ♪♩ | ♩ ♫♩ ♫ | ♩ ♩ ♩ ' | ♩ ♩ ♩ ♩ | ♫♫♫ . A contemporary player might have added a shake to the 6th note of the theme (*e″*) thus: ♩ (= ♫♫♫). The piece is in rounded binary form, for the theme returns in its entirety at the close (starting at the upbeat to b.17).

Source: Musikbibliothek der Stadt Leipzig, Ms. III.8.4.

Gigue

BWV 820/6

Johann Sebastian Bach

The unslurred quavers might be largely detached as a contrast to the slurred groups. Like the Bourrée that precedes it, the piece is in rounded binary form, for the whole of the initial theme returns at the close (starting at the upbeat to b.15).

Source: Musikbibliothek der Stadt Leipzig, Ms. III.8.4.

Menuet

Anon.

This Minuet belongs among the many anonymous pieces that Bach's wife Anna Magdalena copied into her *Clavierbüchlein* of 1725 (see the note to Petzold's Minuets, p. 48).

Suggested phrasing (bb. 1–4):

Source: Berlin (West), Staatsbibliothek Preussischer Kulturbesitz, Mus. ms. Bach P 225 (*Clavierbüchlein* for Anna Magdalena Bach, 1725). Upper stave: soprano clef. The piece is numbered BWV Anh. 132 in Schmieder's catalogue.

Premier Air
pour la Suite du Trophée
Plain Version

François Couperin
(1668–1733)

48a

François Couperin was, alongside Rameau, one of the greatest French composers of the 18th century. Like J. S. Bach, he was the outstanding member of a large family of musicians. He was appointed royal harpsichordist in 1717.

This piece is the first of two Airs that are designed to follow a piece entitled *Le Trophée* (The Trophy). Wilfrid Mellers suggests that the first Air describes victory; the second (in the minor), defeat.

The editorial plain version omits all but the essential ornaments; the ornamented version follows Couperin's original edition. The plain version should be used only for practice purposes and by inexperienced players. Ideally one should progress from the plain to the ornamented version as soon as possible, for Couperin's ornaments are, as always, an integral part of his conception.

Premier Air
pour la Suite du Trophée

Ornamented Version

François Couperin

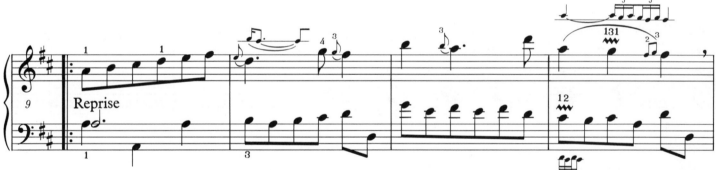

Quavers should be accorded the slight long-short lilt of *notes inégales* (see Introduction, p.7): thus ♪♪♪♪♪♪ = roughly 𝅘𝅥 ♪ 𝅘𝅥 ♪ 𝅘𝅥 ♪ .

Source: *Quatrième Livre de Pièces de Clavecin* (Paris, 1730). Time signature: 3. All slurs take the form ⌒. The commas are Couperin's.
1st bass note of b.8a: crotchet not quaver.

Menuet en Rondeau

Jean-Philippe Rameau
(1683–1764)

Together with François Couperin, Rameau was the most important French composer of the 18th century. His keyboard works are among the boldest and most original products of the French classical school of harpsichord music.

This simple Minuet is designed as a rondeau: the sign 𝄋 in b.16 indicates that the rondeau theme (bb.1–8) returns (without repeats) after the episode or *couplet* (bb.9–16), creating the overall structure ABA. Play the quavers in unequal pairs – roughly ♩♪♪♩♪ (see Introduction, p.7). The fingering is Rameau's own.

Source: *Pièces de Clavecin* (2nd edn; Paris, 1731). Time signature: 3.

Menuet

Jean-Philippe Rameau

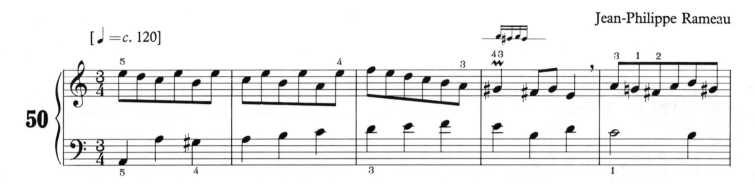

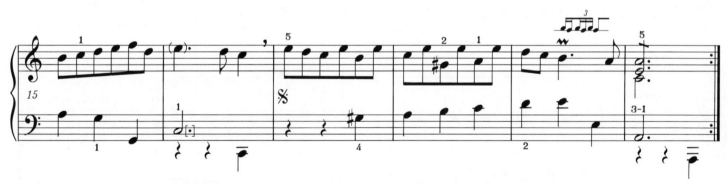

This Minuet displays a facet of Rameau's keyboard style that is remarkably close to that of J. S. Bach.

Largely conjunct quavers should be played unequally (see Introduction, p.7). Thus in the r.h. of b.3 ♪♪♪♪♪♪ = roughly ♩♪♩♪♩♪ . But broken-chordal quavers (e.g. r.h. of bb.1–2) remain equal and may be phrased either ♪♪♪♪♪ or – using *tenuto* touch – ♪♪♪♪♪ . The oblique stroke through the stem in the r.h. of bb.8b & 20 indicates that the chord should be spread downwards in the rhythm ♪♪♪♪ (b.8b) or ♪♪♩ (b.20). The sign ‰ in b.17 denotes the *petite reprise*: bb.17–20 are to be played again as a coda at the very end, after the repeat of the 2nd half as a whole.

Source: *Premier Livre de Pièces de Clavecin* (Paris, 1706). Time signature: 3.

L'Agréable

Plain Version

Jean-François Dandrieu
(*c.* 1682–1738)

Gracieusement [♩ =*c.* 66]

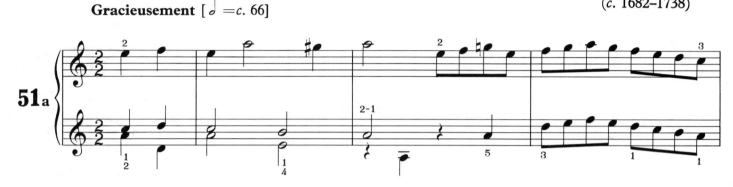

Dandrieu was, from 1721, organist at the royal chapel in Paris. After Couperin and Rameau, he was the most celebrated French harpsichord composer of the 18th century.

L'Agréable is a *Gavotte*: a pastoral French dance in moderate 2/2 or ¢ time, with phrases beginning and ending half-way through the bar. The title and expression mark inform us that an agreeable atmosphere is to be conjured up by graceful playing.

AB 2085

L'Agréable

Ornamented Version

Jean-François Dandrieu

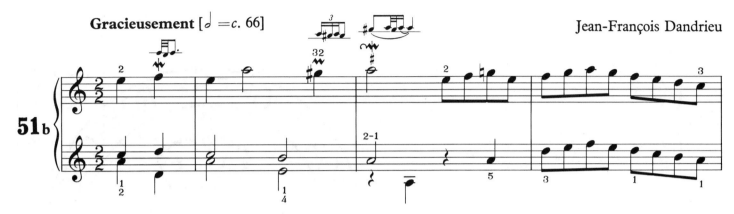

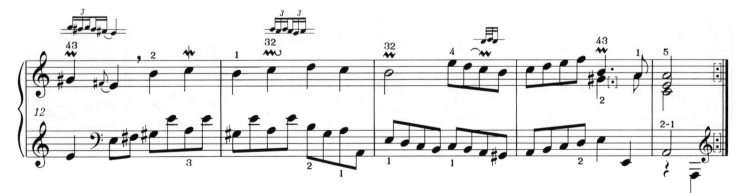

The editorial plain version omits all but the essential ornaments; the ornamented version follows Dandrieu's original edition. Suggested phrasing:
♩ ♩ | ♩ ♩ | ♩ ♩ | ♩ ' ♪♪♪♪ | ♪♪♪♪ ♪♪♪♪ | ♩ . Play the quavers (except broken-chordal ones in the l.h.) unequally: ♫ = roughly ♩♪ (see Introduction, p.7). Spread the r.h. chords in bb.6, 8 & 16 (perhaps the first upwards, the others downwards).

Source: [Ier] *Livre de Pièces de Clavecin* (Paris, 1724). Time signature: 2.

Suite de la Réjouissance

Gavotte en Rondeau

Plain Version

Louis-Claude Daquin
(1694–1772)

52a

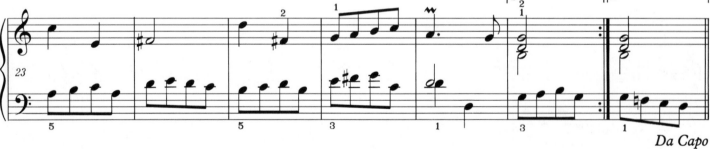

Da Capo

Daquin was very precocious as a child, holding organist's posts in Paris from the age of 12. In 1739 he was appointed *organiste du roi* (royal organist). He was widely regarded as the finest French keyboard player of his generation.

The greater part of Daquin's 4th Suite in C minor/major is taken up with a 7-movement *Divertissement* (entertainment) entitled *Les Plaisirs de la Chasse* (The Pleasures of the Hunt). The second-last movement expresses the rejoicing of the hunters at the success of their sport. The finale – *Suite de la Réjouissance* – continues their rejoicing in a *Gavotte en rondeau* which, in the orginal edition, is followed by four *doubles* or variations.

Suite de la Réjouissance

Gavotte en Rondeau

Ornamented Version

Louis-Claude Daquin

Da Capo

The piece is not notated like a conventional Gavotte, but imagine it barred in 2/2 with a half-bar opening: ♩ ♩ | ♩ ♩ ♩ | ♩ ♩ ♩ | ♩ ♫♫ | ♩ ♩. Crotchets should be staccato in order to throw the stress onto the minims: ♩ ♩ | ♩ etc. Play the quavers in unequal pairs (see Introduction, p.7): roughly ♩♪♪♪ etc.

The piece is designed as a rondeau with a single episode (bb.17–28), so that the structure is ABA. It is given here in two versions: a plain version, in which all but the essential ornaments have been omitted by the editor; and the ornamented version of Daquin's original edition.

Source: *Ier Livre de Pièces de Clavecin* (Paris, 1735). The 1st-time bar, b.28a, is editorial.

Minuetto
Kp.40

Domenico Scarlatti
(1685–1757)

53

[♩ =c. 120]

Domenico Scarlatti, son of the famous Alessandro, was the greatest Italian keyboard composer of the 18th century. He moved to Portugal in 1719 and, nine years later, settled in Spain, where he cultivated a boldly original keyboard style.

This Minuet shows Scarlatti in a gravely expressive mood. Suggested phrasing of bb.1–3: ♪♪ ♩ etc.; and of b.4: ♫♫♫ . The r.h. of bb. 5–6 might be played as if in two parts by employing *tenuto* touch thus: ♪♫♪ | ♪♫ etc.

Source: Roseingrave edn, *XLII Suites de Pièces pour le Clavecin* (London, 1739). Key signature: two flats.

Larghetto

Kp.34

Domenico Scarlatti

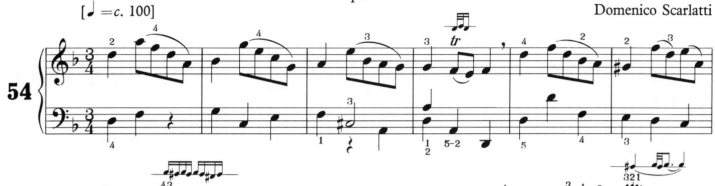

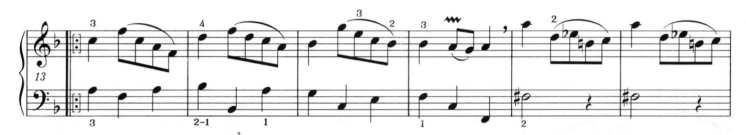

As Ralph Kirkpatrick has remarked, Scarlatti's Neapolitan origins betray themselves in the minuets and other small pieces, such as this *Larghetto*, that appeared in 1739 in a famous edition by his English friend Thomas Roseingrave. In this piece, note the Neapolitan flat supertonic, which is introduced unobtrusively in the 2nd phrase (bb.5–8) but makes a striking effect at the cadence (b.11; see also bb.21–4 & 27 in the 2nd half).

Play in a *legato cantabile* style. The phrasing is quite fully marked by the composer and needs little amplification. Note that the ornament in b.16 should be identical with that of b.4, despite the different sign.

Source: Roseingrave edn, *XLII Suites de Pièces pour le Clavecin* (London, 1739). Key signature: no flat.

Aire

Maurice Greene
(1696–1755)

Maurice Greene was organist of the Chapel Royal and of St Paul's Cathedral. He became Master of the King's Musick in 1735.

The tempo mark of the source – Allegro – is probably mistaken, for this is a slow movement in style. Suggested phrasing: ♩♩♩♩♩ | ♩. etc.
Bb.12–14 contain a sequence of written-out appoggiaturas, to be played thus: ♩♩♩ . The odd-looking ornament of the source, with its double vertical stroke, appears to be a multi-purpose sign, like the cross in Telemann or Mattheson. The essential ornaments are the cadential shakes in bb.4, 7 & 19; the remainder may be treated as optional.

Source: London, British Library, Add. MS 31467.

Printed by
Halstan & Co. Ltd., Amersham, Bucks., England   AB 2085   1/02